This book is dedicated
to my dogfriends Wren and Pip

Pip and Wren

THIS BOOK
BELONGS TO

MASON
+ RYE

from Grammie

"Finse Explores Europe"

The right of Karine Hagen to be identified as the author
and Suzy-Jane Tanner to be identified as the illustrator
of this work has been asserted by them in accordance
with the Copyright Designs and Patents Act 1988.

Text copyright © Karine Hagen 2013
Illustrations copyright © Suzy-Jane Tanner 2013

First published by Viking Cruises
83 Wimbledon Park Side, London, SW19 5LP

ISBN 978-1-909968-01-1

www.finse.me

Reproduction, printing and binding by Colophon Digital Projects Ltd,
Brentford, TW8 8LB, United Kingdom

# FINSE
## EXPLORES EUROPE

Karine Hagen
Suzy-Jane Tanner

NETHERLANDS

GERMANY

*Amsterdam*

_Kinderdijk_

*Cologne*

Rhine

*Bamberg*

*Koblenz*

Moselle

*Nuremberg*

*Regensburg*

N

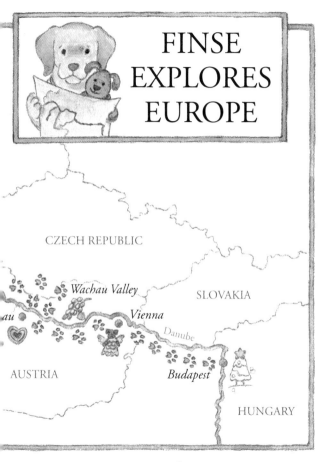

# FINSE
# EXPLORES
# EUROPE

CZECH REPUBLIC

*Wachau Valley*

SLOVAKIA

*Vienna*

Danube

au

AUSTRIA

*Budapest*

HUNGARY

I love springtime, when I play in the wildflower meadow at Highclere Castle with my brothers Scoobie and Alfie.

I decided it was time for me to explore the changing seasons in Europe.

So I set out for Amsterdam to start my journey.

I cycled along the canalside through the city.

Then down the river to Kinderdijk, past tulips, windmills and dogs wearing clogs.

I went on to Cologne where they paint beautiful Easter eggs.

They hang them from trees and everyone collects as many as they can.

I hunted for them near the Cathedral.

9

I enjoyed spending time in Koblenz, a historic city where the Moselle and Rhine rivers meet.

I visited nearby Marksburg Castle. Then I hiked through the countryside and stopped for a picnic.

11

I carried on down the
Middle Rhine, passing
the famous Lorelei Rock.

There is a legend that
a beautiful maiden
sings sweetly there, but
sometimes she lures
sailors to their doom
on the rocks.

In Bamberg I enjoyed the Sandkirchweih Festival. I decorated a bathtub duck and entered it in the duck race.

Then I watched the water jousting. Nearly everyone fell into the river!

In Nuremberg, I took
Fuddlewuddle to meet
the wonderful old toys at
the famous toy museum.

We watched a thrilling
performance at the
summer puppet festival.

17

There are more than a thousand different types of German sausage.

In the medieval town of Regensburg, I tasted several of them at the oldest restaurant in the country.

I reached the beautiful
Wachau Valley on
the Danube River at
harvest time.

I helped gather apricots
and grapes to make the
famous local drinks.

21

My girlfriends Pip and Wren Springer-Spaniel love shopping, so I met them in Passau for the Christmas market.

Bossy Pip decided we should all buy the local gingerbread as gifts.

Then she ate most of hers!

23

At the Christmas market in Vienna, there were carved figures and knitted angels.

By the end of the day, we were rather tired. Pip was determined that a large slice of Sachertorte would soon revive us!

We bought more gifts at the Christmas market in Budapest. It was very cold so we enjoyed some warming ginger punch.

Then we watched Santa arrive. Pip informed him exactly what presents she expected for Christmas!

I returned to Highclere
Castle for the holidays.

I put the gifts I had bought
for all the family under the
tree in the Great Hall.

We opened our presents
together on Christmas
morning.

There was one for me!
A globe! How wonderful!

It is just what I need to
plan my next adventure.

# DOGOLOGY

Finse met many breeds of dog on her travels through Europe, most of them native